DIANA:
PRINCESS
OF THE
AMAZONS

DIANA: PRINCESS OF THE AMAZONS

WRITTEN BY
**SHANNON HALE
& DEAN HALE**

ILLUSTRATED BY
VICTORIA YING

COLORS BY **LARK PIEN**
LETTERS BY **DAVE SHARPE**

WONDER WOMAN CREATED BY WILLIAM MOULTON MARSTON

LAUREN BISOM Editor
STEVE COOK Design Director – Books
AMIE BROCKWAY-METCALF Publication Design

BOB HARRAS Senior VP – Editor-in-Chief, DC Comics
MICHELE R. WELLS VP & Executive Editor, Young Reader

DAN DiDIO Publisher
JIM LEE Publisher & Chief Creative Officer
BOBBIE CHASE VP – New Publishing Initiatives & Talent Development
DON FALLETTI VP – Manufacturing Operations & Workflow Management
LAWRENCE GANEM VP – Talent Services
ALISON GILL Senior VP – Manufacturing & Operations
HANK KANALZ Senior VP – Publishing Strategy & Support Services
DAN MIRON VP – Publishing Operations
NICK J. NAPOLITANO VP – Manufacturing Administration & Design
NANCY SPEARS VP – Sales

DIANA: PRINCESS OF THE AMAZONS

DC Comics, 2900 West Alameda Ave.,
Burbank, CA 91505
Printed by LSC Communications,
Crawfordsville, IN, USA.
11/29/19. First Printing.
ISBN: 978-1-4012-9111-2
School Market Edition ISBN:
978-1-77950-407-4

Library of Congress Cataloging-in-Publication Data

Names: Hale, Shannon, writer. | Hale, Dean, 1972- writer. | Ying, Victoria,
    illustrator. | Pien, Lark, colourist. | Sharpe, Dave (Letterer),
    letterer.
Title: Diana, Princess of the Amazons : a graphic novel / written by
    Shannon Hale & Dean Hale ; illustrated by Victoria Ying ; colors by Lark
    Pien ; letters by Dave Sharpe.
Description: Burbank, CA : DC Comics, [2020] | "Wonder Woman created
    William Moulton Marston" | Audience: Ages 8-12 | Audience: Grades 4-6
    Summary: Eleven-year-old Diana, the gangly, sometimes clumsy, only ch
    on the island of Themyscira, struggles to live up to the high Amazonian
    standards and longs for someone her own age whom she can talk to.
Identifiers: LCCN 2019040273 (print) | LCCN 2019040274 (ebook) | ISBN
    9781401291112 (paperback) | ISBN 9781779500892 (ebook)
Subjects: LCSH: Graphic novels. | CYAC: Graphic novels. |
    Loneliness--Fiction. | Self-esteem--Fiction. | Amazons--Fiction.
Classification: LCC PZ7.7.H35 Di 2020 (print) | LCC PZ7.7.H35 (ebook) |
    DDC 741.5/973--dc23

TABLE OF CONTENTS

For the kids who look up to Auntie Gal
and the former kids who spun
alongside Auntie Lynda.

—Shannon and Dean Hale

For Lily.

—Victoria Ying

CHAPTER ONE

Making a Friend

Over three thousand years ago, the gods placed the Amazons on the Paradise Islands and hid them from the rest of the world.

But there's plenty to do here for kids like me.

It's spring, and everywhere I look, mother animals are caring for their young.

But when they start growing up, it all changes.

=SQUEAK!=

Yep, plenty to do. For kids.

If there were any other kids.

Hello, Princess.

Hi, Auntie Dessa.

My mother, Queen Hippolyta, has always been ruler of the Amazons.

Every single person on the Paradise Islands is thousands of years old but never ages.

So it was a big huge deal when I was born.

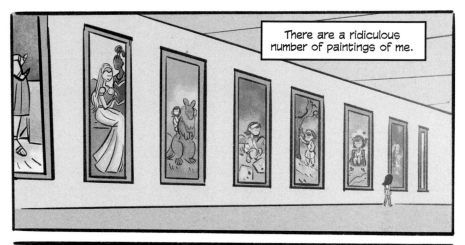

There are a ridiculous number of paintings of me.

Well, paintings of little me. There haven't been any recently.

15

Here's another thing about being the only kid: There are a lot of aunties to notice when you do something wrong.

And to tell on you.

Diana, what has come over you lately? This is not how Amazons behave.

Sorry.

For breaking her pot, you will spend the afternoon helping the stable master.

But...you promised we could play slap ball today.

I'll meet you there later.

17

General Antiope pairs all the warriors with a partner who matches their size and ability.

My mother says I'm too young to start training.

Besides, there's no one Antiope could pair with me.

21

22

CHAPTER TWO

Cutting Class
on Themyscira

35

39

40

41

44

Everything about Themyscira feels new and exciting with someone to share it with.

Mona even likes to help me count the wildlife—something none of the grown-ups seem to care about.

THUMP

SPLOSH!

Gah!

I'm filthy! Filthy!

51

Why does that small island have such a big dock?

Oh! Well... there's this thing there called Doom's Doorway.

Doom's Doorway is a gate into Tartarus!

What is that?

Tartarus is like...a monster jail.

So there are monsters behind the door?

The souls of monsters go into Tartarus after they're defeated. They only become solid again if they escape.

But the gods placed the Amazons on the Paradise Islands to guard the doorway, so that will never happen.

Mona said if I got caught skipping out on my tutor, I'd get in so much trouble.

She said it isn't fair that I'm hounded while the rest of the Amazons are free.

She said it didn't sound like my mother respects me, not like she respects her sister Amazons.

I don't know. Maybe she's right.

Diana, the healer says you aren't injured at all.

I don't know why you lied, but I am surprised by you, Diana. Worse, I'm disappointed.

No matter how perfect I try to be, I'll never truly be one of them.

65

CHAPTER
THREE

Only an Amazon

Once again, I'm not so sure about this.

But everywhere, I see Amazons doing amazing things.

Things my mother won't let me be part of. Because I'm too young?

Or because she thinks that I'm not a real Amazon?

75

This feels like just another game we're playing.

Shhhh...

A sneaking game.

A hiding game.

A hunting game.

79

Come on...

BOOM
BOOM
BOOM

Something big is coming.

BOOOM

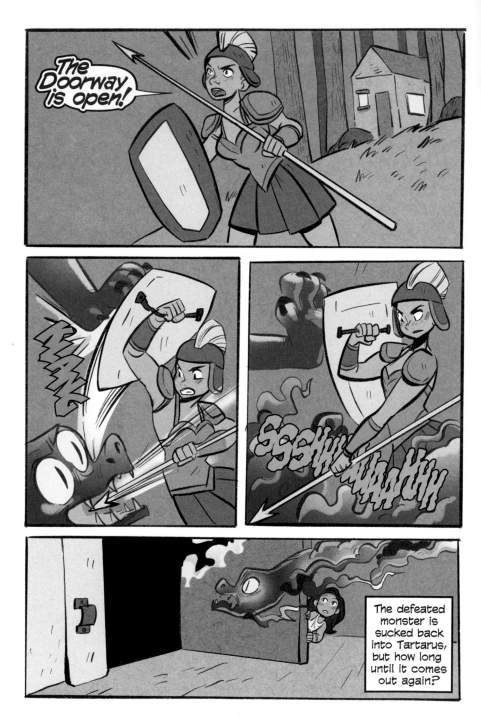

94

This is all
my fault.

CHAPTER FOUR

The Best of Us

Circe is more dangerous than all the monsters. Stop her first!

Your turn, Hippolyta.

With no new monsters emerging, the Amazons from Themyscira are able to defeat the rest.

Oink.

Change them back.

Whyever would I do that?

Return them to how they were, Circe, and I swear I will let you leave unscathed.

You swear? Swear by what?

And so, Diana of Themyscira, you are hereby ordered to make reparations for the damage you helped cause.

That's fair. I'm really, really sorry.

We know, Diana.

In addition to your punishment, the council has chosen to entrust you with a new responsibility.

You will be Themyscira's first wildlife steward, cataloging and counting the animals of the island.

Report back to us about their needs.

I will. Thank you.

132

Shannon and Dean Hale are the husband-and-wife writing team behind Eisner nominee *Rapunzel's Revenge* (illustrated by Nathan Hale), *New York Times* bestselling series *The Princess in Black* (illustrated by LeUyen Pham), and two novels about Marvel's Squirrel Girl. Shannon Hale is also the author of the Newbery Honor-winning novel *Princess Academy*, the *USA Today* bestselling *Ever After High* series, the graphic novel memoir *Real Friends*, and others. Shannon and Dean live in Utah with their four children, who all agree that Wonder Woman is one of the greatest superheroes of all time.

Victoria Ying is an author and artist living in Los Angeles. She started her career in the arts by falling in love with comic books, which eventually turned into a career working in animation. She loves Japanese curry, putting things in her shopping cart online and taking them out again, and hanging out with her dopey dog. Her film credits include *Tangled, Wreck-It Ralph, Frozen, Paperman, Big Hero 6*, and *Moana*. She has illustrated several picture books including *Not Quite Black and White; Lost and Found, What's That Sound?*; and *Take a Ride By My Sid*e, and is the writer and illustrator of *Meow! Diana: Princess of the Amazons* is her debut graphic novel.

Lark Pien is an award-winning cartoonist and picture book author. She occasionally performs color work for unique comics that inspire. *Diana: Princess of the Amazons* is her first coloring project with an all-female cast! The naughty, the nice, the brave and capable, she's enjoyed coloring them all.

There's a certain house on a certain street that everyone talks about.

142

Anyway, a senior center's not Broadway, but it's a gig.

You know, before she got sick your mom *dreamed* of making it to the big stage...

Anyone can do the big smoke-and-mirrors stuff but a magician who makes things disappear by speaking *backward* is...

Cheesy?

Epic.

You're going to blow the roof off the Shady Oaks Retirement Center.

COO-KOo!

I'm running late!

145

147

148

152

153

And the school nurse said it was probably some kind of allergic reaction, but what allergy turns people bright *red!*

It was *freaky.*

I was such a jerk to Benji today. Totally brushed him off.

All because Margo doesn't think I'm cool enough to hang with the cool kids.

Then I come home and Dad's looking like he went ten rounds with Killer Croc.

What's he hiding?

Bet Mom would've seen right through Dad's bogus story.

But I bet she was never a jerk to her friends either.

You know what? We're *done* moping!

155

What? This is a letter from Mom!
My dearest love,
Thank you for the latest news about our daughter.
I miss her so, but I know you are doing the best you can without me.
It's hard being a single fath
a teenage girl, but
doing a wonderful job
She called me a *teenage* girl?
Wait, she's... alive?